ACTIVITY
ANNUAL

Pedigree®

Published 2008
Published by Pedigree Books LTD, Beech Hill House,
Walnut Gardens, Exeter, Devon EX4 4DH
books@pedigreegroup.co.uk

£5.99

YODA

Homeworld: **Unknown**

Species: **Unknown**

Gender: **Male**

Height: **0.66 meters**

Weapon: **Lightsaber**

Affiliation: **Jedi**

Yoda was the oldest and wisest of all the Jedi. At nine hundred years old Yoda had learned more about the Force than any other Jedi. He lived his final years on the swamp planet of Dagobah where he trained Luke Skywalker. He had trained many Jedi knights in his lifetime, most notably Obi-Wan Kenobi and Anakin Skywalker.

Yoda served a most important role on the Jedi Council. When young Padawans began their early Jedi training, they did so under the watchful eye of Master Yoda. As the shadow of the dark side fell over the Republic in its twilight years, Yoda grew increasingly concerned. The Jedi Council dispatched Obi-Wan Kenobi to discover exactly what was afoot. What he discovered was an entire clone army created for the Republic. Unbeknownst to the Jedi, Count Dooku, one of Yoda's former Padawans, had turned to the dark side of the Force and was behind the military force.

Yoda and Dooku engaged in battle. First, their Force powers were put to test, as Dooku attempted to crush the tiny Jedi Master with hurled debris. Yoda easily deflected such assaults, and even repulsed Dooku's Sith lightning attacks. The contest came down to a duel of lightsabers. In a climactic battle, the two master combatants displayed amazing speed and agility. Yoda, empowered by the Force, leaped through the air, twirling and battering at Dooku's defences. Dooku only managed to escape by using the Force to once again jeopardise Anakin and Obi-Wan. Knowing that Yoda's nobility would buy him time, Dooku fled as the ancient Jedi Master saved his younger compatriots.

Many years later, Yoda would train perhaps the greatest Jedi Knight of all, Luke Skywalker. Through Yoda's training, Luke became powerful enough to reinstate order to the Force and defeat the evil Emperor. Although Yoda died before he could see Luke fulfil his destiny, at the celebration after the Battle of Endor, Luke saw the spectre of Yoda, joined by ghostly images of Obi-Wan Kenobi and Anakin Skywalker, signifying that all was right with the Force.

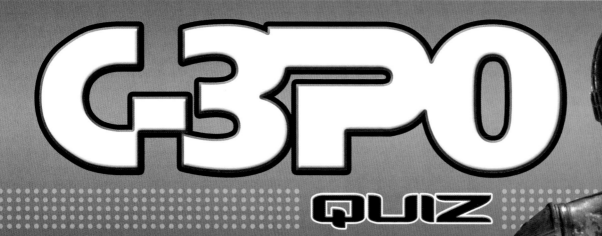

C-3PO QUIZ

QUESTION 1

What is this odd looking fellow's name?

A	DARTH MAUL	☑
B	CLIEGG LARS	☐
C	JAR JAR BINKS	☐

QUESTION 2

On what planet were the clone troopers created?

A	TATOOINE	☐
B	MUSTAFAR	☐
C	KAMINO	☑

QUESTION 3

Who was Boba Fett's father?

A	JABBA	☒
B	JANGO	☑
C	ZAM	☒

"Hello there. I am C-3PO, human cyborg relations, but you can call me Threepio. I am here to help you learn all about the *Star Wars* universe and to educate you on such matters as what you must never say to a Tusken Raider and how to become friendly with an Ewok! Take my quiz and by the end of this book you will be ready to become a fully fledged member of the Rebel Alliance!"

QUESTION 4

What is the first line of the Jedi Code?

A THERE IS NO EMOTION ☑

B THERE IS NO IGNORANCE ☐

C THERE IS NO DEATH ☐

QUESTION 5

Who trained Master Ki-Adi-Mundi?

A MACE WINDU ☑

B YODA ☑

C QUI-GON JINN ☑

Q6

Where did Palpatine come from?

A NABOO ☐

B RUUSAN ☐

C TOYDARIA ☐

QUESTION 7

Which species might carry a boomer into battle?

A THE EWOKS ☐

B THE GUNGANS ☐

C THE DUGS ☐

QUESTION 8

Can you match each lightsaber to its owner?

A   B   C

DARTH MAUL ☑   COUNT DOOKU ☑   MACE WINDU ☑

QUIZ

Q 9 ▶

Can you tell which Jedi Knight this is?

A	OBI WAN	☒
B	QUI-GON JINN	☒
C	LUKE SKYWALKER	☑

QUESTION 10

Who did Darth Maul first reveal himself to?

A	JAR JAR BINKS	☒
B	QUI-GON JINN	☑
C	QUEEN AMIDALA	☒

Q 11

Where did Luke Skywalker find Yoda?

A	DAGOBAH	☑
B	NABOO	☐
C	TATOOINE	☐

Q 12

What was the name of Qui-Gon Jinn's first Padawan?

A	XANATOS	☐
B	OBI-WAN	☑
C	ANAKIN	☐

QUESTION 13

What is the name of the underwater city where the Gungans live?

A OTOH GUNGA ✓

B OTHO GUNGA ☐

C ORTHO GUNGA ☐

QUESTION 14

Who does this spaceship belong to?

A HAN SOLO ☐

B JABBA THE HUTT ☐

C BOBA FETT ☑

Q 15

Who lives on the Forest Moon of Endor?

A THE GAMORREANS ☐

B THE EWOKS ☑

C THE WOOKIEES ☐

QUESTION 16

Which bounty hunter did Leia disguise herself as to gain entry to Jabba's palace?

A GREEDO ☐

B JANGO FETT ☐

C BOUSHH ☐

LUKE SKYWALKER

Homeworld: Tatooine

Species: Human

Gender: Male

Height: 1.72 meters

Weapon: Lightsaber, blaster pistol

Vehicle: X-wing starfighter

Affiliation: Rebel Alliance, Jedi, Rogue squadron

As a simple moisture farmer on the desert planet Tatooine, Luke Skywalker often dreamt of galactic adventure. You would often find him staring at the twin moons of Tatooine and imagining what it would be like to one day leave his home.

When Luke discovered a distress call from Princess Leia Organa programmed into a droid his uncle had just bought, Luke soon found himself in the midst of an epic battle between the Rebel Alliance and the evil Empire. Luke's path eventually led him to an elderly Jedi Knight, Obi-Wan Kenobi. Obi-Wan would teach Luke the ways of the mystical powers of the Force and the ways of the Jedi.

Obi-Wan, Luke, Han Solo and Chewbacca saved the Princess from the Death Star, in which she was imprisoned, but in the process Obi-Wan fell at the hands of his old apprentice, Darth Vader, leaving Luke to continue his training under the tutelage of Master Yoda. In an effort to turn the young Jedi to the dark side, Darth Vader lured the apprentice away from his training and revealed that he was his father, Anakin Skywalker.

As the last of the Jedi and the final hope for the galaxy, Luke had to face his darkest fears in a deadly confrontation with his father and his father's master, the Emperor. While the final battle between the Empire and the Rebel Alliance raged on, Luke battled his father in a violent lightsaber duel, eventually cutting off his father's hand. It was at this point that the Emperor joined the fight using his powers of the dark side. It looked as though Luke was doomed until at the last moment, the final remnants of good left in his father awakened. Darth Vader attacked his master, throwing him into a deep shaft within the Death Star. Anakin Skywalker had re-emerged to save his son but sacrificed his life in the process.

Anakin's redemption and Luke's personal triumph saved the galaxy and restored freedom and justice to millions.

yoda's JEDI trials

QUESTION 1

A disturbance in the Force you feel. What do you do?

A FIND THE CAUSE OF THE DISTURBANCE AND DESTROY IT. ☐

B SEEK GUIDANCE FROM THE JEDI COUNCIL. ☐

C IGNORE IT. IT IS NOT YOUR PROBLEM. ☐

QUESTION 2

You suspect a Jedi of turning to the dark side. What do you do?

A ASK THE JEDI COUNCIL FOR ADVICE. ■

B CONFRONT THE JEDI IN QUESTION. ■

C PULL OUT YOUR LIGHTSABER. IF HE ATTACKS, YOU WILL BE READY. ■

Training to become a Jedi is no easy feat my young Padawan. Many challenges there are to face. Use the Force you must. Clear your mind and answer these questions to find out what your future holds.

QUESTION 3

What is your most prized possession?

A NOTHING. MATERIAL THINGS MEAN NOTHING TO YOU. ☐

B YOUR LIGHTSABER. ☑

C YOUR FAMILY. ☐

QUESTION 4

You sense that your friends are in danger but the Jedi Council has told you to stay where you are. Do you?

A IGNORE THE COUNCIL AND GO TO RESCUE YOUR FRIENDS. ☐

B DO WHAT THE COUNCIL ASK OF YOU. ☐

C EXPLAIN YOUR FEELINGS TO THE COUNCIL AND ASK FOR THEIR HELP. ☑

QUESTION 5

You are chasing a Sith Lord but you lose him. What do you do?

A USE THE FORCE AND TRY AND DETECT WHERE HE IS. ☑

B RETURN TO BASE AND GIVE UP. ☐

C KEEP LOOKING. YOU WILL FIND HIM IF IT TAKES ALL NIGHT. ☐

QUESTION 6

Your R2 unit is hit by laser fire. It has been a faithful servant to you since you were a young Padawan. Do you?

A FORGET ABOUT IT AND BUY A NEW ONE. ☐

B REPAIR THE DROID AND MAKE IT GOOD AS NEW. ☑

C SELL OFF THE PARTS TO THE JAWAS. ☐

Add up your scores and carry them over to the next challenge.
1. A=6, B=10, C=2 **2.** A=10, B=6, C=2 **3.** A=6, B=2, C=10 **4.** A=6, B=2, C=10 **5.** A=10, B=2, C=6 **6.** A=2, B=10, C=6

WORD SEARCH

Find all ten words in this Word Search and prove that you have a keen enough eye to become a Jedi! Answers can be forwards, backwards, vertical, horizontal or diagonal.

X	B	L	V	A	P	G	G	K	Z	Z	O	D	L	E
B	W	E	Z	E	C	E	H	J	B	L	Q	U	D	N
S	E	I	U	W	F	C	H	T	I	S	K	T	F	I
J	M	L	N	Q	G	O	A	C	Y	E	H	Z	B	T
W	H	V	L	G	L	Q	T	B	S	L	V	W	B	A
Q	T	P	L	O	C	D	U	K	W	I	I	X	Z	P
L	I	H	S	F	X	M	Y	T	W	E	H	P	B	L
C	G	N	U	L	A	W	G	A	B	F	H	H	H	A
M	A	I	B	C	A	W	I	N	D	U	F	C	Y	P
H	X	F	E	L	Z	G	R	Z	U	U	O	M	O	K
G	N	J	K	H	S	X	F	B	A	I	R	D	C	R
T	C	E	O	M	X	F	V	B	I	U	C	V	C	F
I	R	A	T	S	H	T	A	E	D	Y	E	D	H	U
W	N	U	J	A	C	C	A	D	F	C	K	A	P	V
S	H	P	O	Q	I	M	L	R	E	G	L	W	J	Q

CHEWBACCA

DEATH STAR

FORCE

HAN SOLO

LUKE SKYWALKER

MACE

PALPATINE

SITH

WINDU

X WING

CROSS WORD

Use your Jedi Mind Powers to solve the cryptic clues and find all the dark side enemies.

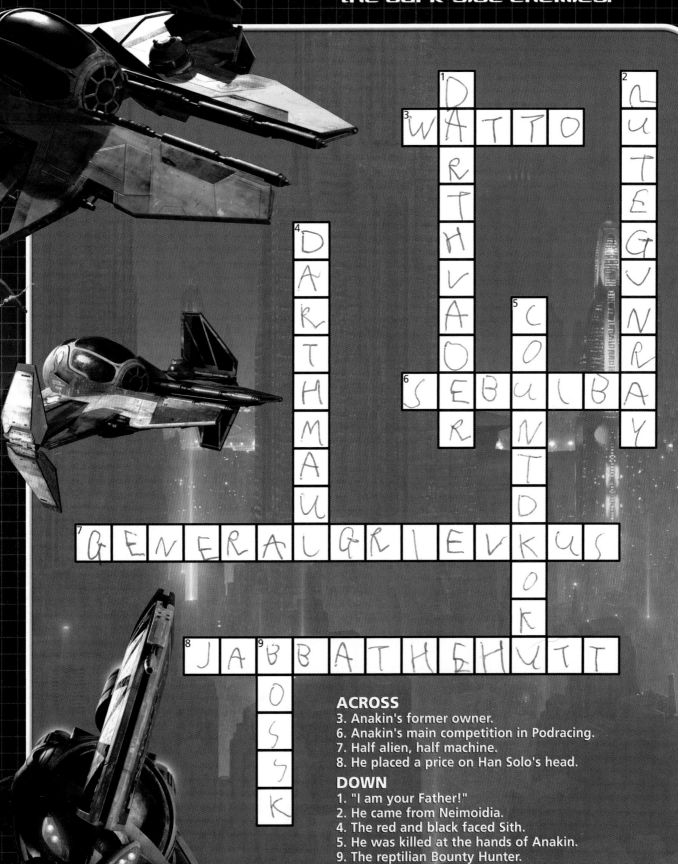

ACROSS
3. Anakin's former owner.
6. Anakin's main competition in Podracing.
7. Half alien, half machine.
8. He placed a price on Han Solo's head.

DOWN
1. "I am your Father!"
2. He came from Neimoidia.
4. The red and black faced Sith.
5. He was killed at the hands of Anakin.
9. The reptilian Bounty Hunter.

OBI-WAN KENOBI

Obi-Wan Kenobi was a dedicated and legendary Jedi Knight. His long and sometimes tumultuous career helped to shape the fate of an entire galaxy. When he was just 25 years old he got caught up in important events at the Battle of Naboo. At the time he was still learning his craft under the watchful eye of his Jedi Master, Qui-Gon Jinn. Before the battle Obi-Wan followed his master to the planet of Tatooine. It was here that Qui-Gon Jinn discovered a young slave boy, Anakin Skywalker. Qui-Gon Jinn believed that Anakin was the Chosen One who would fulfil an ancient Jedi prophecy. Obi-Wan was quite taken aback when Qui-Gon Jinn told him he wanted to take young Anakin as his Padawan, replacing Obi-Wan, who Qui-Gon felt was ready to become a Jedi Knight. This was just one of the few arguments Obi-Wan and Qui-Gon Jinn had.

Species: **Human**

Gender: **Male**

Height: **1.79 meters**

Weapon: **Lightsaber**

Vehicle: **Jedi starfighter**

Affiliation: **Jedi**

Obi-Wan Kenobi did indeed take Anakin as his Padawan but he always felt that there was something awry with the young Jedi. During the Clone Wars, Obi-Wan ascended to the rank of Jedi Master and took a seat on the Jedi Council. Obi-Wan and Anakin were later sent to rescue Chancellor Palpatine from Count Dooku, whom they had previously battled on Geonosis. Aboard the starship *The Invisible Hand*, Anakin and Obi-Wan cut their way through droid forces as they raced to free the Chancellor. It was certainly a trap, but the Jedi had no shortage of confidence in their abilities, as indicated by Obi-Wan's strategy: "Spring the trap."

Later, the two Jedi would battle Darth Maul. During the battle, Obi-Wan became separated from his Master allowing Darth Maul to slay Qui-Gon Jinn. A devastated Obi-Wan managed to kill the Sith Lord in turn. Qui-Gon Jinn's dying wish was for Obi-Wan to continue training Anakin in the ways of the Force.

They found the Chancellor bound to a chair in the spacious observation deck of the ship. Waiting for them was Count Dooku, and unlike the impulsive and disorganized attack of their last confrontation with Dooku, Obi-Wan and Anakin challenged the Sith Lord as a team.

Dooku proved a formidable opponent. He Force-pushed Obi-Wan with terrible strength, tossing the Jedi Master like a rag doll against the wall of the quarters. Kenobi was knocked unconscious. Out cold, he never saw the final moments of the duel, where Anakin killed an unarmed Dooku in cold blood at the Chancellor's goading, a stark warning of things to come.

R2-D2

Homeworld: Naboo

Species: Droid

Height: 0.96 meters

Manufacturer: Industrial Automaton

Type: Astromech droid

Weapon: Arc welder, buzz saw

Vehicle: X-wing, Naboo N-1 starfighter

Affiliation: Rebel Alliance

The ever faithful R2-D2 is more than your average astromech droid. This R2 unit has a feisty personality, an unusual characteristic for a typical utility droid. Artoo's resourcefulness has made him invaluable to his friends on numerous occasions.

R2-D2 comes from the peaceful world of Naboo, where he and a team of astromechs served Queen Amidala aboard her Royal Starship. When the greedy Trade Federation invaded Naboo, Amidala rushed away from her world and ran afoul of a blockade. When the Royal Starship sustained damage to its shields, it was R2-D2 who repaired the ship, allowing it to escape into hyperspace. The droid used his magnetised rollers to cling tenaciously to the chromed surface of the ship while deadly turbolaser blasts rained overhead. For his courage, Artoo was personally thanked and recognised by Queen Amidala.

Years later, Artoo and C-3PO would find themselves in the service of the Royal House of Alderaan. The influential family of nobles had secret ties to the burgeoning Rebel Alliance. While intercepting transmissions from Rebel spies, the Organa consular ship was suddenly attacked by an Imperial Star Destroyer laying in wait. The transmission carried information vital to the Rebellion: the complete technical read-outs of the Empire's latest weapon of mass-destruction, the Death Star battle station. Unable to deliver the plans to Viceroy Bail Organa, Leia Organa instead hid them in Artoo's memory systems. She also tasked Artoo to continue her other mission, that of contacting the long-lost Jedi Knight and Republic General, Obi-Wan Kenobi.

C-3PO QUIZ

QUESTION 17

What was Luke Skywalker's aunt named?

A	BERU	☐
B	PADMÉ	☐
C	SHMI	☑

QUESTION 18

Who used Banthas as a mode of transport?

A	THE GEONOSIANS	☐
B	THE SAND PEOPLE	☐
C	THE WOOKIEES	☑

QUESTION 19

What was the name of Chewbacca's home planet?

A	KASHYYYK	☐
B	ALDERAAN	☑
C	GEONOSIS	☐

QUESTION 20

How many complete *Millennium Falcons* can you make from these shapes?

A	2	☐
B	3	☐
C	5	☐

QUESTION 21

How many lightsabers did General Grievous wield against Obi-Wan Kenobi?

| A | 2 | ☐ | B | 3 | ☐ | C | 4 | ☑ |

QUESTION 22

Who is this?

A	DARTH SIDIOUS	☐
B	NUTE GUNRAY	☑
C	POGGLE THE LESSER	☐

QUESTION 23

What was Aurra Sing's occupation?

A	A STARFIGHTER PILOT	☐
B	A SMUGGLER	☐
C	A BOUNTY HUNTER	☑

QUESTION 24

Who was the Prime Minister of Kamino?

A	LAMA SU	☐
B	ZAM WESELL	☐
C	MON MOTHMA	☐

C-3PO QUIZ

QUESTION 25

What was the name of Luke's childhood friend who died during the first attack on the Death Star?

A MON MOTHMA ☐

B BIGGS DARKLIGHTER ☐

C ADMIRAL PIETT ☐

QUESTION 26

How many storm troopers made up a battalion?

A 850 ☐

B 900 ☐

C 820 ☐

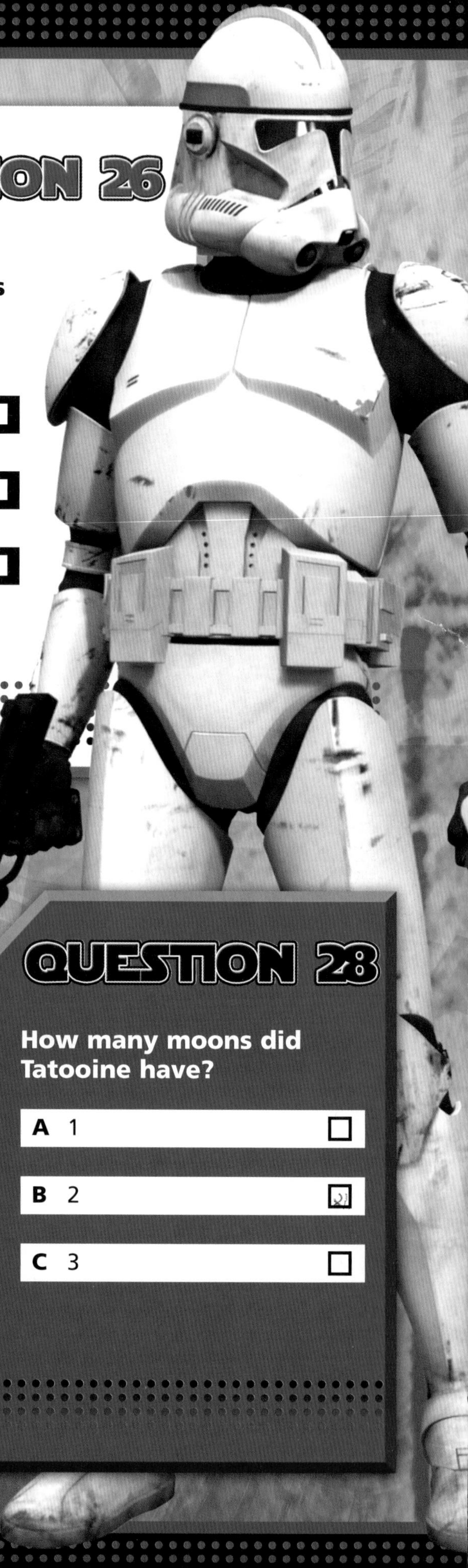

QUESTION 27

Who sold R2-D2 and I to Owen Lars?

A THE SAND PEOPLE ☐

B THE JAWAS ☐

C OBI-WAN KENOBI ☐

QUESTION 28

How many moons did Tatooine have?

A 1 ☐

B 2 ☒

C 3 ☐

QUESTION 29

What was the name of the canyon where Luke honed his flying skills as a child?

A BLAGGER'S CANYON ☐

B BEGGAR'S CANYON ☐

C JANNER'S CANYON ☐

QUESTION 30

Which of these pieces does it take to make a complete Death Star?

A ☑   B ☐   C ☐

QUESTION 31

Can you match the Jedi to their lightsaber?

A

B

C

DARTH VADER ☐   OBI-WAN KENOBI ☐   YODA ☐

Q 32

What kind of planet was Kamino?

A A FOREST PLANET ☐

B AN OCEAN PLANET ☐

C A DESERT PLANET ☐

Millennium Falcon

Homeworld: Corellia
Size: 26.7 meters long
Manufacturer: Corellian Engineering Corporation
Type: YT-1300 freighter
Weapons: Quad laser cannons, concussion missiles
Affiliation: Rebel Alliance

TIE Fighter

Size: 6.3 meters long
Manufacturer: Sienar Fleet Systems
Type: Starfighter
Weapon: Laser cannons
Affiliation: Galactic Empire

X-wing Fighter

Size: 12.5 meters long
Manufacturer: Incom Corporation
Type: Starfighter
Weapons: Laser cannons, proton torpedoes
Affiliation: Rebel Alliance

HOW MUCH DO YOU KNOW ABOUT SOME OF THE VEHICLES USED IN THE *STAR WARS* UNIVERSE? DO YOU KNOW HOW BIG THE DEATH STAR IS AND THAT ITS SUPERLASER COULD DESTROY AN ENTIRE PLANET IN A MATTER OF SECONDS?

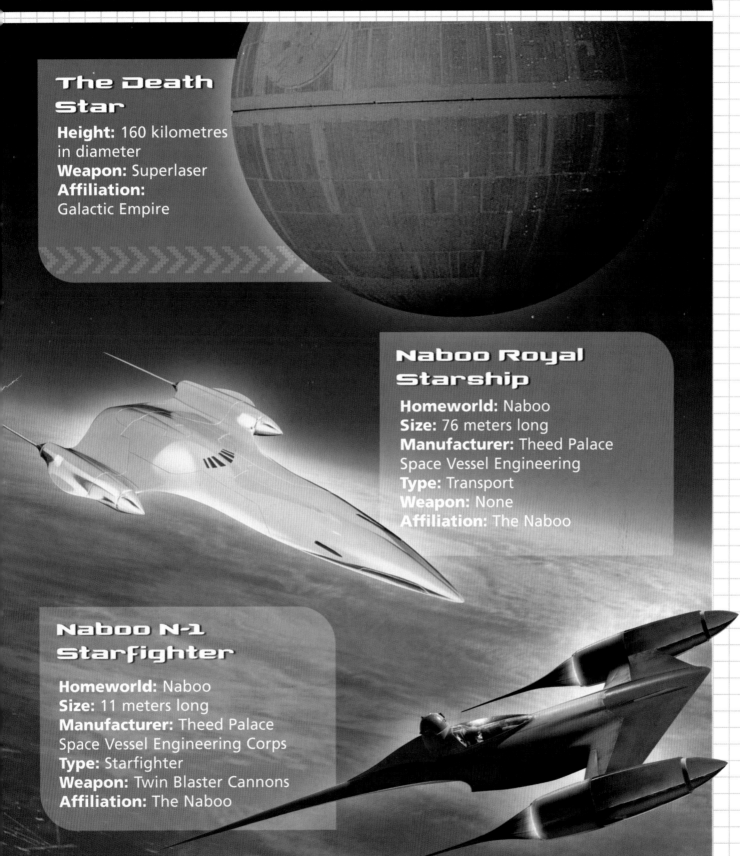

The Death Star

Height: 160 kilometres in diameter
Weapon: Superlaser
Affiliation:
Galactic Empire

Naboo Royal Starship

Homeworld: Naboo
Size: 76 meters long
Manufacturer: Theed Palace Space Vessel Engineering
Type: Transport
Weapon: None
Affiliation: The Naboo

Naboo N-1 Starfighter

Homeworld: Naboo
Size: 11 meters long
Manufacturer: Theed Palace Space Vessel Engineering Corps
Type: Starfighter
Weapon: Twin Blaster Cannons
Affiliation: The Naboo

PADMÊ AMIDALA

Homeworld: **Naboo**

Species: **Human**

Gender: **Female**

Height: **1.65 meters**

Weapon: **Royal pistol**

Vehicle: **Naboo Royal Starship,
Naboo Royal Cruiser, Naboo yacht,
Naboo star skiff**

Affiliation: **The Naboo, Galactic Senate**

Padmé Naberrie was born in a small mountain village on the planet Naboo. As a child it was apparent that she was very gifted and she soon joined the Apprentice Legislature at age 11. By 14, she was elected Queen of Naboo. As per the traditions of Naboo she adopted the name of state Amidala. After she had severed her term as Queen, Padmé became a Senator for Naboo, working hard to achieve peace and stability for the galaxy. She led the opposition against the Military Creation Act but on the day that the act was to be passed, her ship was attacked. This led to her being placed under the protection of the Jedi, more specifically, Obi-Wan Kenobi and his Padawan, Anakin Skywalker, who Padmé had not seen in nearly a decade.

Anakin took Padmé to Naboo to protect her while the other Jedi Knights investigated the attacks against her. It was here that the two of them rekindled their friendship and soon fell in love. Both tried to ignore their feelings as it went again the Jedi laws that Anakin had promised to follow but it was to no avail. After the Battle of Geonosis, Anakin and Padmé were married in a secret ceremony with C-3PO and R2-D2 as their witnesses.

Eventually, Padmé fell pregnant. When she told Anakin that they were going to be parents, he started to have vivid and powerful dreams that Padmé would die during childbirth. He simply could not let that happen. His fears led him to the dark side in the hope that he could develop his powers enough to save his wife or even bring her back to life.

Obi-Wan Kenobi told Padmé that Anakin had turned to the dark side of the Force. Padmé could not believe what she had been told and took her ship to Mustafar to confront her husband. Obi-Wan stowed away on the ship without Padmé knowing and when they arrived at Mustafar he attacked his former Padawan. Anakin assumed that Padmé had brought Obi-Wan with her to kill him and in his rage he attacked his wife with a Force chokehold. As Obi-Wan and Anakin duelled, C-3PO and R2-D2 carried Padmé onto her starship. Her medical team worked to keep her alive but Anakin had broken her heart and her spirit. Before she passed, she gave birth to twins, Luke and Leia. Yoda, Bail Organa and Obi-Wan vowed to keep the children safe.

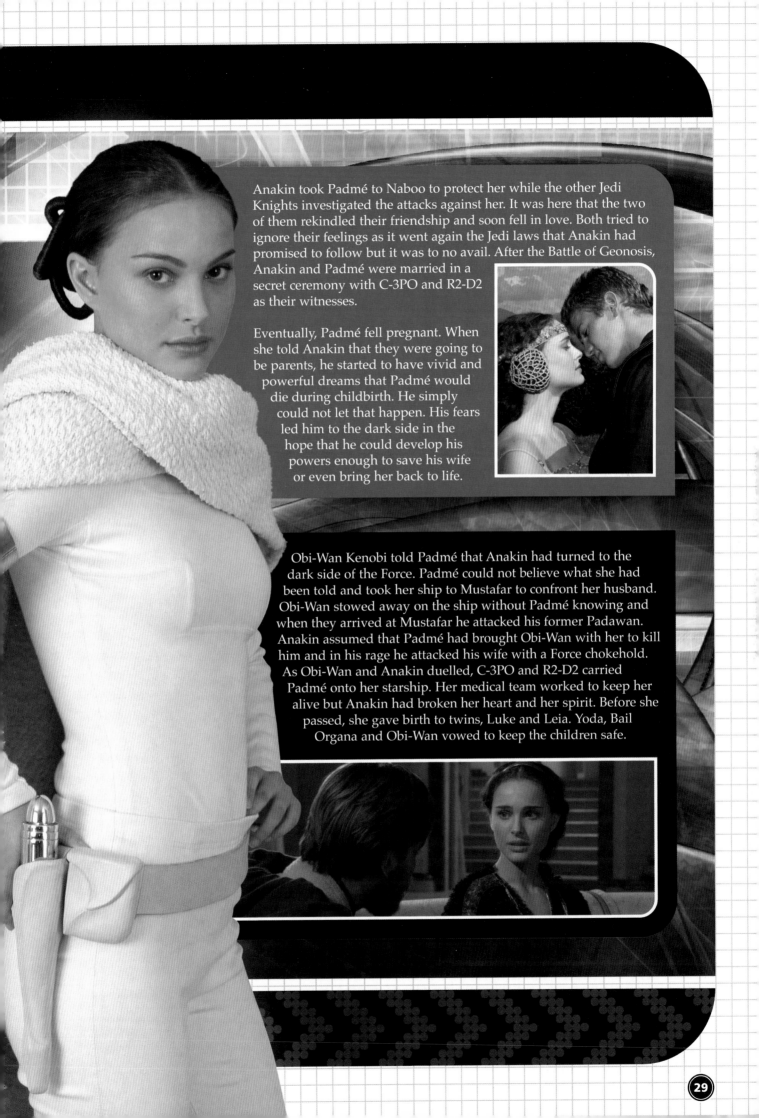

MACE WINDU

Homeworld: Haruun Kal

Species: Human

Gender: Male

Height: 1.88 meters

Weapon: Lightsaber

Affiliation: Jedi Council

Mace Windu was a highly revered senior member of the Jedi Council. He shared the same concerns as Yoda regarding the continuing disturbances in the Force and the deterioration of the Republic. Mace was a diplomat by nature but when it came time to do battle he certainly knew how to handle a lightsaber. In fact, he even invented his own fighting style named the Vaapad technique. Some thought that the style was too aggressive and even went as far as to suggest it came close to dark side practices. That said, it was certainly effective. Mace Windu had only ever been defeated twice in lightsaber duels. Once by Master Yoda and another time by Count Dooku.

Windu was well-versed in the Jedi teachings and prophecies. When Qui-Gon Jin discovered Anakin and brought him to the Jedi Temple, Windu already knew that Qui-Gon suspected Anakin of being the Chosen One. Windu did not agree and after consultation with the Jedi Council, announced that Anakin would not be trained. After Qui-Gon Jin died, the council reversed its decision but Windu remained suspicious of the young Skywalker.

Windu's suspicions were confirmed when he was dispatched to capture Chancellor Palpatine who had revealed himself as Darth Sidious, the Sith Lord that had escaped Jedi detection all this time. It was Anakin Skywalker who loyally delivered news of this discovery to Windu, though the Jedi Master still did not fully trust the young Jedi. Mace gathered a team of his finest Jedi warriors -- Saesee Tiin, Agen Kolar and Kit Fisto -- to arrest the Chancellor. Though Skywalker wished to accompany Windu, the Jedi Master forbade it. He ordered Skywalker to stay in the Council chambers until the matter was resolved.

Windu had disarmed Darth Sidious and was about to deliver a fatal blow to the Dark Lord when Anakin arrived. Anakin cut off Windu's arm, leaving him defenceless against Darth Sidious' attack. The Sith Lord attacked Mace Windu with bolts of Sith lightning eventually sending him into the Coruscant skies and to his death in the city below.

yoda's JEDI trials

QUESTION 7

Your ship is hit while flying over a populated area. Do you?

A STEER THE SHIP AWAY FROM ANY HOUSES BEFORE EJECTING. ☐

B FLY YOUR SHIP INTO AN ENEMY STRONGHOLD. ☐

C CLOSE YOUR EYES AND HOPE FOR THE BEST. ☐

QUESTION 8

Your Jedi Master asks you to do something that seems impossible. Do you?

A GET ANGRY THINKING THAT YOUR MASTER IS TRYING TO MAKE YOU LOOK FOOLISH. ☐

B TRY YOUR BEST TO COMPLETE THE TASK. ☐

C TELL YOUR MASTER THAT HE IS ASKING YOU TO DO SOMETHING THAT YOU CAN'T. ☐

QUESTION 9

The Jedi Council tells you that they suspect your Master of turning to the dark side. Do you?

A TELL THE COUNCIL THEY ARE WRONG. ☐

B LISTEN TO WHAT THE COUNCIL HAS TO SAY AND KEEP AN EYE ON YOUR MASTER. ☐

C TELL YOUR MASTER THAT THE COUNCIL SUSPECTS HIM. ☐

The second part of your training you have reached, but more difficult your challenges will now become!

QUESTION 10

During battle your best friend is hit by blaster fire. Do you?

A FORGET ABOUT THE BATTLE AND HELP YOUR FRIEND. ☐

B TAKE OUT YOUR ANGER ON YOUR ENEMY. ☐

C CALL FOR HELP WHILE PROTECTING YOUR FRIEND FROM FURTHER ATTACK. ☐

QUESTION 11

You are told that you are the "Chosen One" and that you will one day save the entire galaxy. How does this make you feel?

A FLATTERED AND EXCITED ABOUT THE FUTURE. ☐

B SCARED, THE PRESSURE IS TOO MUCH. ☐

C NEUTRAL. YOU WANT TO REMAIN FOCUSED ON YOUR TRAINING AND SEE WHAT THE FUTURE HOLDS. ☐

QUESTION 12

You lose your lightsaber that was given to you by Master Yoda, what do you do?

A BUILD YOURSELF A NEW ONE AND HOPE NOBODY NOTICES. ☐

B ASK MASTER YODA FOR FORGIVENESS AND BE MORE CAREFUL NEXT TIME. ☐

C LIE AND TELL MASTER YODA IT WAS STOLEN BY THE SITH. ☐

Add up you scores from this round and the first one, and then move on to the final stage of your training
7. A=10, B=6, C=2 **8.** A=2=B=10, C=6 **9.** A=6, B=10, C=2 **10.** A=6, B=2, C=10 **11.** A=6, B=2, C=10 **12.** A=6, B=10, C=2

STAR WARS

HAN SOLO

Homeworld: Corellia

Species: Human

Gender: Male

Height: 1.8 meters

Weapon: Heavy blaster pistol

Vehicle: Millennium Falcon

Affiliation: Rebel Alliance

Han Solo was a smuggler born on Corellia. Before entering into the smuggling world he enrolled in the Imperial Academy but his stubbornness and belief in fairness soon got him into trouble. One incident involved a slave Wookiee who was being mistreated by his handlers. Solo stood up for the Wookiee and his insubordination led to him being expelled from the Academy. After his expulsion he rescued the Wookiee named Chewbacca and the two became inseparable friends. Solo had a penchant for gambling in his early days and he won the *Millennium Falcon* from a gambling buddy named Lando Calrissian. The *Falcon* was in disrepair but between Han and Chewie, they made it into one of the fastest ships in the galaxy.

To earn money Han ran a regular glitterstim spice smuggling route for Jabba the Hutt. On one such mission his ship was boarded by Imperial customs officials and he had to dump his load. Jabba was furious and demanded that Han repay him. To do so, Han offered to fly some passengers to Alderaan for a largely inflated price. Those passengers would turn out to be Obi-Wan Kenobi and Luke Skywalker. Before he knew it, Han was involved with rescuing Princess Leia from the evil Darth Vader. He would also help Luke to eventually destroy the dreaded Death Star. He became known as one of the heroes of Yavin for his role in the first decisive victory the Rebels has gained over the Empire.

Solo spent the next few years assisting the Rebel Alliance in their missions against the Empire. Soon his past would catch up with him when he was trapped on Cloud City by Darth Vader and encased in carbonite. Jabba the Hutt had put a price on his head and the bounty hunter, Boba Fett, took his carbonised body back to Jabba's palace where it remained as a trophy until Leia released him.

Solo would go on to lead a mission to Endor to disable the newly constructed Death Star's defensive shield. The mission was a success thanks in part to the native Ewoks who joined the Rebel Alliance to defeat the Imperial stormtrooper army. After the Death Star was destroyed, Han finally declared his true feelings for Leia and the two would become an integral part of the new Galactic Republic.

STAR WARS ANAGRAMS

Use the Force to try and decipher these coded messages sent by the Rebel Alliance before the Empire beats you to it. Remember, there is no try, there is only do or do not.

1 IM DAWN CUE
☐☐☐☐☐ ☐☐☐☐☐

2 HARD ADVERT
☐☐☐☐☐☐ ☐☐☐☐☐

3 LEAKY SKEW LURK
☐☐☐☐☐
☐☐☐☐☐☐☐☐☐

4 APE DIAL MADAM
☐☐☐☐☐
☐☐☐☐☐☐☐

5 AWAKE KINKY SNARL

6 WEAK ONION BIB

7 ALARM THUD

8 DUN COOKOUT

9 JAR NARK JIBS

10 OH LOANS

CHEWBACCA

Chewbacca was born on the forest planet of Kashyyyk. Years before he became first mate on the *Millennium Falcon* he fought alongside Master Yoda in the Clone Wars. He remained loyal to the Jedi when Palpatine gave Order 66, and when the clone troopers turned on the Jedi Knights, Chewbacca helped save Yoda from certain death. Shortly after the Clone Wars, Chewbacca was captured by the Empire and enslaved at a hard-labour camp until he was rescued by an impetuous young Imperial Cadet going by the name of Han Solo.

Homeworld: Kashyyyk

Species: Wookiee

Gender: Male

Height: 2.28 meters

Weapon: Bowcaster

Vehicle: *Millennium Falcon*

Affiliation: Rebel Alliance

After Han had been forced to leave the Academy, Chewbacca joined him and swore a 'life debt" to the man who had saved him. He became the protector and best friend of the quick-talking Corellian and served with Solo as the two of them became a well-known smuggling duo working for some of the biggest crime organisations in the galaxy. When they came into ownership of the freighter *Millennium Falcon*, their exploits became legendary.

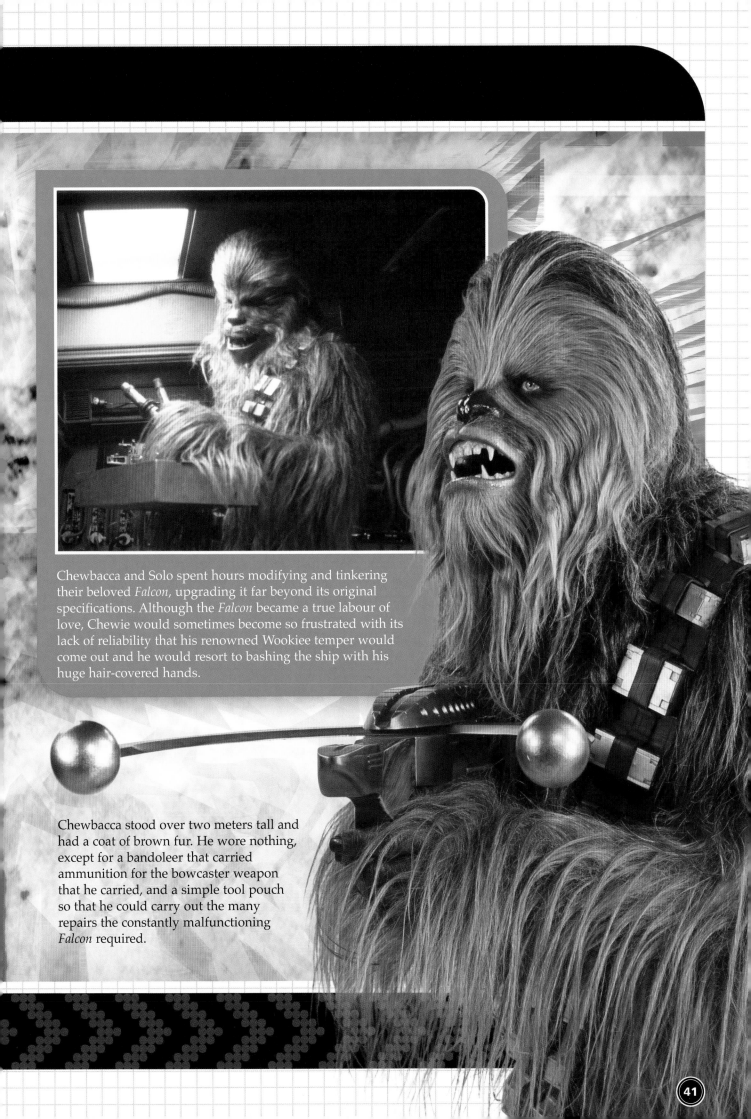

Chewbacca and Solo spent hours modifying and tinkering their beloved *Falcon*, upgrading it far beyond its original specifications. Although the *Falcon* became a true labour of love, Chewie would sometimes become so frustrated with its lack of reliability that his renowned Wookiee temper would come out and he would resort to bashing the ship with his huge hair-covered hands.

Chewbacca stood over two meters tall and had a coat of brown fur. He wore nothing, except for a bandoleer that carried ammunition for the bowcaster weapon that he carried, and a simple tool pouch so that he could carry out the many repairs the constantly malfunctioning *Falcon* required.

STARSHIP EXAM

Size: 12.5 meters long
Manufacturer: Incom Corporation
Type: Starfighter
Weapon: Laser cannons, proton torpedoes
Affiliation: Rebel Alliance
Associations:
Wedge Antilles
Biggs Darklighter (Red Three)
R2-D2 (Artoo-Detoo)
Red Leader
Luke Skywalker

1:

Size: 26.7 meters long
Manufacturer: Corellian Engineering Corporation
Type: YT-1300 freighter
Weapon: Quad laser cannons, concussion missiles
Affiliation: Rebel Alliance
Associations:
Lando Calrissian, Chewbacca
Nien Nunb, Han Solo

2:

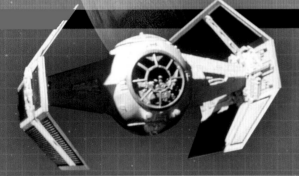

Size: 6.3 meters long
Manufacturer: Sienar Fleet Systems
Type: Starfighter
Weapon: Laser cannons
Affiliation:
Galactic Empire

3:

Size: 19,000 meters
Manufacturer:
Kuat Drive Yards
Type: Cruiser
Affiliation: Galactic Empire
Associations:
Imperial Navy Troopers
Admiral Piett
Darth Vader

4:

FROM THE DESCRIPTIONS BELOW CAN YOU WORK OUT THE NAME OF EACH SHIP? IF YOU CAN, YOU ARE WELL ON YOUR WAY TO BECOMING A FULLY FLEDGED MEMBER OF THE REBEL ALLIANCE FIGHTER SQUADRON.

Size: (Delta-7) 8 meters long; (Eta-2) 5.47 meters long
Manufacturer: Kuat Systems Engineering
Type: Light interceptor starfighter
Weapon: (Delta-7) laser cannons; (Eta-2) dual laser cannons; 2 secondary ion cannons
Affiliation: Jedi
Associations: Obi-Wan Kenobi, Anakin Skywalker

5:

Size: 21.5 meters long
Manufacturer: Kuat Systems Engineering
Type: Pursuit vessel
Weapon: Laser cannons, concealed projectile launchers, ion cannons, tractor beam
Affiliation: Bounty hunter
Associations:
Boba Fett, Jango Fett

6:

DARTH VADER

Darth Vader was a Dark Lord of the Sith and apprentice to Emperor Palpatine. He was one of the most feared men in the entire galaxy, ruthlessly hunting down the few remaining Jedi in hiding on far flung planets. It had not always been this way, though. Vader was born Anakin Skywalker on the planet of Tatooine. His mother revealed to Qui-Gon Jinn that he had never had a biological father. This fulfilled one of the ancient Jedi prophecies of the Chosen One. Qui-Gon Jinn took the young Anakin to the Jedi Council and eventually took him to be his apprentice. When Qui-Gon Jinn was killed, his dying wish was that Obi-Wan Kenobi continue the Padawan's training. Obi-Wan took care of the young Jedi, teaching him the ways of the Force.

Eventually, Anakin would be tempted by the dark side of the Force in an attempt to save the love of his life, Padmé Amidala. Once the dark side of the Force had taken hold of the young Jedi, he slaughtered all the younglings at the Jedi Temple before inadvertently killing Padmé. He fought Master Obi-Wan on the fiery planet of Mustafar but his skills were not up to that of his former teacher and he was defeated and hideously burned in the molten rock pools that covered the surface of the planet. He was saved only when Emperor Palpatine found his almost unrecognisable body and took him to an Imperial rehabilitation centre. It was here where his gnarled and amputated torso was fused with artificial limbs and encased in a fearsome black suit. He was kept alive by an artificial respirator and an undying hatred channelled from the dark side of the Force.

Years later at the Battle of Yavin, Vader would battle his son who he had believed to have perished many years ago on Mustafar. This discovery led to Vader eventually turning on his master and saving his son before once again becoming one with the Force. As he lay dying, Vader ceased to be. Anakin Skywalker returned. He asked his son to remove the cumbersome, fearsome mask that had concealed his face for decades. His mask and life support removed, Anakin looked upon Luke for the first and last time. He then died, his body disappearing into the light side of the Force. Luke burned the dark armour that had encased Anakin's crippled body in a quiet funeral pyre on the forest moon of Endor that night.

C-3PO QUIZ

QUESTION 33

On what planet was Darth Vader born?

A	ALDERAAN	☐
B	TATOOINE	☐
C	KASHYYYK	☐

QUESTION 34

How many TIE fighters can you make from these shapes?

A	1	☐
B	2	☐
C	3	☐

QUESTION 35

On which planet would you find Mos Eisley?

A	TATOOINE	☐
B	MYGEETO	☐
C	CORUSCANT	☐

QUESTION 36

Whose arm did Obi-Wan Kenobi severe at the Outlander Club on Coruscant?

A GREEDO'S ☐

B ZAM WESELL'S ☐

C JANGO FETT'S ☐

QUESTION 37

What was the name of the beast Jabba kept under his palace?

A RANCOR ☐

B BANTHA ☐

C DUNGA ☐

QUESTION 38

Who was the leader of the Gungans?

A BOSS NASS ☐

B JAR JAR BINKS ☐

C POGGLE THE LESSER ☐

QUESTION 39

Which of these battle droids is the odd one out?

A ☐

B ☐

C ☐

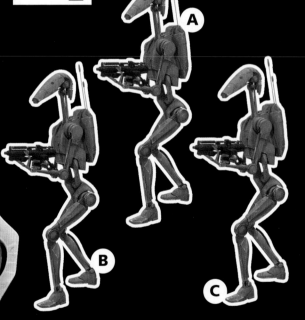

QUESTION 40

Where would you find Echo Base?

A ALDERAAN ☐

B HOTH ☐

C ENDOR ☐

C-3PO QUIZ

QUESTION 41

Which Jedi Knight had a R4-P17 droid built into his Jedi starfighter?

- **A** QUI-GON JINN ☐
- **B** OBI-WAN KENOBI ☐
- **C** MACE WINDU ☐

QUESTION 42

On which planet would you find a Blurrg?

- **A** ENDOR ☐
- **B** MUSTAFAR ☐
- **C** TATOOINE ☐

QUESTION 43

What are the Ithorians better known as?

- **A** BULLETHEADS ☐
- **B** HAMMERHEADS ☐
- **C** NAILHEADS ☐

QUESTION 44

How many eyes does a Gran have?

- **A** 1 ☐
- **B** 2 ☐
- **C** 3 ☐

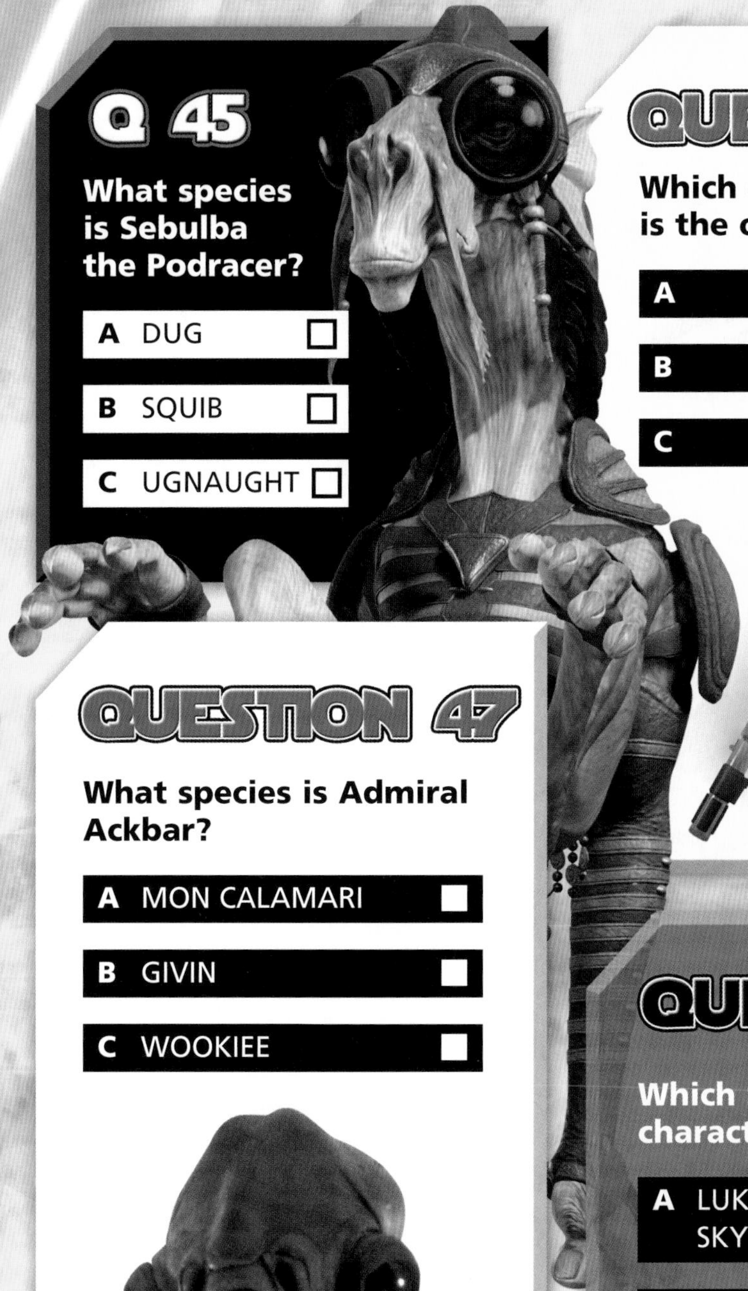

QUIZ

Q 45

What species is Sebulba the Podracer?

A DUG ☐

B SQUIB ☐

C UGNAUGHT ☐

QUESTION 46

Which of these lightsabers is the odd one out?

A ✓

B ✓

C ✗

A   B   C

QUESTION 47

What species is Admiral Ackbar?

A MON CALAMARI ☐

B GIVIN ☐

C WOOKIEE ☐

QUESTION 48

Which Star Wars character is this?

A LUKE SKYWALKER ☐

B PRINCESS LEIA ☐

C HAN SOLO ✓

PALPATINE

Homeworld: **Naboo**

Species: **Human**

Gender: **Male**

Height: **1.73 meters**

Weapon: **Sith lightning**

Vehicle: **Imperial shuttle**

Affiliation: **Galactic Senate, Galactic Republic, Galactic Empire, Sith**

Senator Palpatine came from the idyllic planet of Naboo. When taxes were increased on the planet's outlying trade routes, the powerful Trade Federation imposed a blockade on the planet. Naboo's Queen, Amidala, was rescued by Qui-Gonn Jinn and Obi-Wan Kenobi, and travelled to Coruscant to convince the Galactic Senate to intervene on behalf of her besieged homeworld. It was then that Senator Palpatine convinced Amidala to move for a Vote of No Confidence in Chancellor Valorum. Amidala thought she was doing the right thing, but this move would prove to be the beginning of Palpatine's rise to power. Soon Palpatine was elected as Supreme Chancellor and he promised to put and end to corruption in the Senate. During this time, Palpatine befriended a young Padawan, Anakin Skywalker, and watched as the boy's skills developed.

However, over the next decade the Republic descended further into chaos while the Separatist movement, led by Count Dooku, grew in strength. Palpatine was given emergency powers to create a clone army to act against the Separatists, the likes of which had never been seen before. The army was supposed to protect the Republic but eventually, Palpatine would use the army to destroy the Jedi and help turn the Republic into the Galactic Empire.

Palpatine revealed himself to be the Sith Lord, Darth Sidious, and took Anakin as his apprentice. When Anakin was defeated by Obi-Wan Kenobi on the fiery planet of Mustafar, Palpatine saved him from a certain death and transformed him into the monstrous Darth Vader.

yoda's JEDI trials

QUESTION 13

The Jedi Council tell you that you are not yet ready to become a Jedi Knight. How do you react?

A YOU TELL THE COUNCIL THAT THEY ARE WRONG AND DO NOT KNOW WHAT THEY ARE TALKING ABOUT. ■

B YOU ACCEPT THE COUNCIL'S DECISION REALISING THAT YOUR TIME WILL COME. ■

C YOU LEAVE THE JEDI ORDER AND JOIN THE DARK SIDE. ■

QUESTION 14

You discover that your father is a Sith Lord. How does it make you feel?

A ASHAMED. YOU WANT KILL YOUR FATHER TO BRING HONOUR BACK TO YOUR NAME! ■

B ANGRY. YOU WISH THE JEDI COUNCIL HAD TOLD YOU EARLIER. ■

C RELIEVED. AT LEAST NOW YOU KNOW HOW YOUR FATHER IS. ■

QUESTION 15

Jedi are not allowed any emotional attachment but you fall in love. What do you do?

A KEEP YOUR LOVE SECRET AND DEFY THE JEDI CODE. ☐

B LEAVE THE JEDI ORDER FOR YOUR ONE TRUE LOVE. ☐

C EXPLAIN YOUR SITUATION TO THE JEDI COUNCIL AND SEE WHAT THEIR ADVICE IS. ☐

The final part of your training you have reached! Challenges harder yet, they will become. Let your fear control you do not. Use the Force, young Jedi.

QUESTION 16

You come across a new alien species that seems outwardly aggressive. What do you do?

A DRAW YOUR LIGHTSABER AND GET READY TO FIGHT. ☐

B USE YOUR JEDI MIND POWERS TO COMMUNICATE WITH THE ALIEN. ☐

C WAIT TO SEE WHAT THE ALIENS' NEXT MOVE WILL BE. ☐

QUESTION 17

You are put in a position where to save a family member you must let a whole planet be destroyed. What do you do?

A SAVE YOUR FAMILY MEMBER AND FORGET ABOUT THE PLANET. ☐

B TRY YOUR BEST TO SAVE YOUR FAMILY MEMBER AND THE PLANET. ☐

C SAVE THE PLANET AND SACRIFICE YOUR FAMILY MEMBER. ☐

QUESTION 18

You are in the bar at Jabba's palace and a drunken customer challenges you to a fight. What do you do?

A IGNORE THE CUSTOMER UNTIL HE GOES AWAY. ☐

B DRAW YOUR LIGHTSABER AND CUT OFF HIS ARM. ☐

C USE YOUR JEDI MIND TRICKS TO EMBARRASS THE CUSTOMER. ☐

That is it! You have competed your training. Do you have what it takes to become a Jedi?

Q13. A=6, B=10, C=2
Q14. A=2. B=6, C=10
Q15. A=2, B=6, C-=10
Q16. A=2, B=10, C=6
Q17. A=2, B=10, C=6
Q18. A=10, B=2, C=6

Now add up your scores and see how advanced a Jedi you have become.

170-180 = You are the Chosen One!
150-170 = Jedi Master
100-150 = Jedi Knight
80 - 100 = Not yet ready to become a Jedi.
Less that 80 = You have joined the dark side.

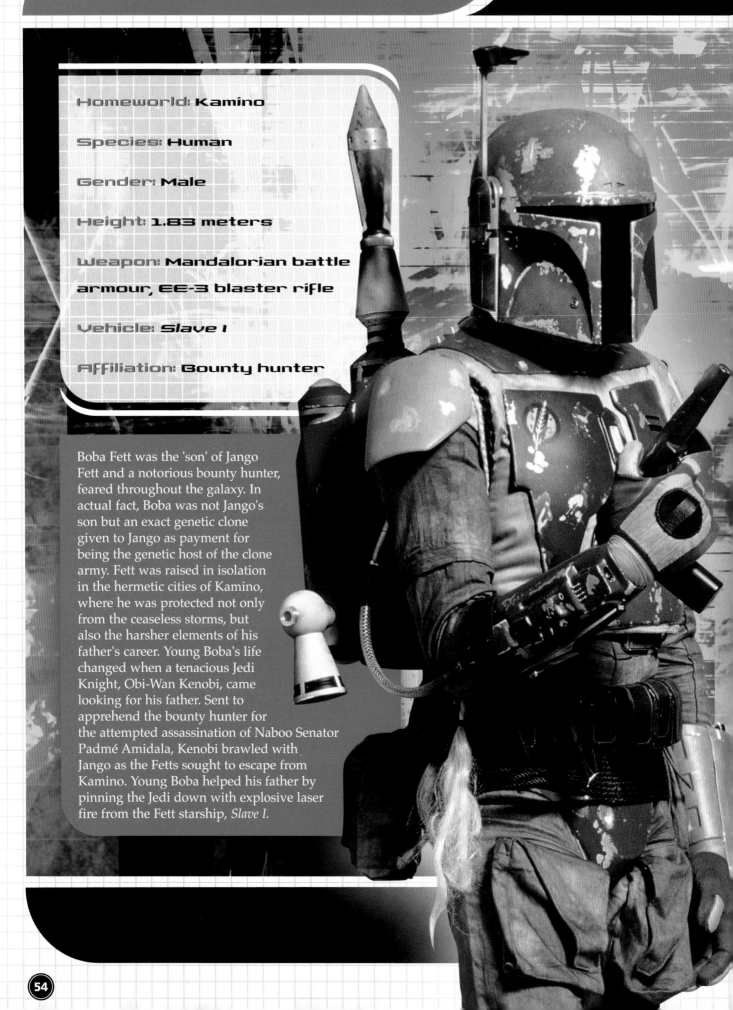

BOBA FETT

Homeworld: Kamino

Species: Human

Gender: Male

Height: 1.83 meters

Weapon: Mandalorian battle armour, EE-3 blaster rifle

Vehicle: Slave I

Affiliation: Bounty hunter

Boba Fett was the 'son' of Jango Fett and a notorious bounty hunter, feared throughout the galaxy. In actual fact, Boba was not Jango's son but an exact genetic clone given to Jango as payment for being the genetic host of the clone army. Fett was raised in isolation in the hermetic cities of Kamino, where he was protected not only from the ceaseless storms, but also the harsher elements of his father's career. Young Boba's life changed when a tenacious Jedi Knight, Obi-Wan Kenobi, came looking for his father. Sent to apprehend the bounty hunter for the attempted assassination of Naboo Senator Padmé Amidala, Kenobi brawled with Jango as the Fetts sought to escape from Kamino. Young Boba helped his father by pinning the Jedi down with explosive laser fire from the Fett starship, *Slave I.*

Fleeing from Kamino, the Fetts journeyed to Geonosis, where Jango's benefactor resided. Boba watched as his father's enemies were sentenced to death, but Jedi prove very hard to kill. A huge battle erupted as Jedi reinforcements stormed Geonosis to free their fellow Jedi. Jango entered the fray, only to be killed by Jedi Master Mace Windu. Boba was shocked to witness his father's swift death, and he quietly cradled Jango's empty helmet as Geonosis erupted into all-out war.

It was Fett who, years later, successfully tracked the *Falcon* from Hoth to Bespin. Arriving at the gas giant before the ship, Fett and Vader sprung a trap on the hapless crew. Fett, a shrewd negotiator, received his bounty for capturing the crew, but also was given custody of Han Solo. The bounty hunter was set to collect the reward on Solo's head placed there by the vile gangster Jabba the Hutt.

Whisking the carbonite-frozen form of Han Solo away from Bespin, Fett eventually arrived on Tatooine aboard his starship, *Slave I*. Fett delivered Solo to Jabba, his sometime employer, and was many thousands of credits richer. Fett stayed at Jabba's palace, and was present when Solo's friends attempted to rescue the carbon-frozen smuggler.

JABBA THE HUTT

Homeworld: Nal Hutta, Tatooine

Species: Hutt

Gender: Neither

Height: 3.9 meters long

Weapon: Assassins and bounty hunters

Vehicle: Ubrikkian luxury sail barge

Affiliation: Criminal

Jabba was a Hutt gangster and criminal mastermind who lived on the desert planet of Tatooine. He had amassed a huge fortune through various illegal activities including smuggling and slavery. From his desert palace on Tatooine he ruled a vast criminal empire that controlled most of the space ports, towns and villages on the planet. Jabba inherited a great deal of wealth from his father, Zorba, but most of his fortune was earned through intimidation and criminal activities. Jabba's palace was guarded by the Gamorreans, a pig-like alien warrior race that served Jabba with undying loyalty.

Jabba's palace was a squalid, immoral den of iniquity that attracted criminals from across the galaxy looking for a place to drink, be entertained and perhaps find work. One of the criminals who found his way to Jabba's palace was a young Han Solo. He ran a smuggling ring with Jabba but on one fateful mission, Han had to jettison his illegal load to avoid being captured by the Empire. The loss of this transport cost Jabba a considerable amount of money and, infuriated, the repulsive, slug like crime lord. Jabba put a huge bounty on Han's head, which was almost collected by Greedo, one of Jabba's bounty hunters. Han killed Greedo but could not escape the Hutt. At the same time a man named Obi-Wan Kenobi and a young Luke Skywalker were looking for a passage to Alderaan. Jabba allowed Han to transport the passengers in return for the proceeds from the charter. Han never returned, instead becoming part of the Rebel Alliance, fighting the evil Empire.

Jabba was eventually killed by Princess Leia who, after a failed attempt to rescue a frozen Han from his carbonite prison adorning the wall of Jabba's palace, was being held captive as a slave girl. Leia, Han, Luke and the others escaped before Jabba's ship exploded and his body was consumed by the flames.

C-3PO

QUIZ

QUESTION 49

What do the initials AT-AT stand for?

A ALL TERRAIN ALIEN TRANSPORT ☐

B ATTACK TROOPER ARMOURED TRANSPORT ☐

C ALL TERRAIN ARMOURED TRANSPORT ☐

QUESTION 50

On which planet did the Rebel Alliance modify their T-47 airspeeders to become snowspeeders?

A ALDERAAN ☐

B HOTH ☐

C MUSTAFAR ☐

QUESTION 51

◀ **Who is this?**

A PADMÉ ■

B LEIA ■

C LUKE SKYWALKER ■

QUESTION 52

What form of lightsaber combat did master Yoda specialise in?

A	FORM IV	☐
B	FORM V	☐
C	FORM VI	☐

QUESTION 53

Which villainous character used a sail barge to entertain his guests?

A	PALPATINE	☐
B	DARTH MAUL	☐
C	JABBA THE HUTT	☐

QUESTION 54

What was the name of Senator Palpatine's ever present aid?

A	SLY MOORE	■
B	AK-REV	■
C	MELAS	■

QUESTION 55

Who killed Qui-Gon Jinn?

A	DARTH VADER	☐
B	DARTH SIDIOUS	☐
C	DARTH MAUL	☐

QUESTION 56

Who told Luke to go to Dagobah to find Yoda?

A	OBI-WAN KENOBI	☐
B	QUI-GON JINN	☐
C	MACE WINDU	☐

C-3PO QUIZ

QUESTION 57

Who was Anakin's owner before Qui-Gon Jinn freed him from slavery?

- **A** WATTO ☐
- **B** JABBA THE HUTT ☐
- **C** SEBULBA ☐

QUESTION 58

Whose Podracer is this?

- **A** SEBULBA'S ☐
- **B** ANAKIN'S ☐
- **C** HEKULA'S ☐

QUESTION 59

What is this ship called?

- **A** TIE BOMBER ☐
- **B** TIE FIGHTER ☐
- **C** TIE INTERCEPTOR ☐

QUESTION 60

What was the name of Nute Gunray's home planet?

- **A** NEIMOIDIA ☐
- **B** MUSTAFAR ☐
- **C** NABOO ☐

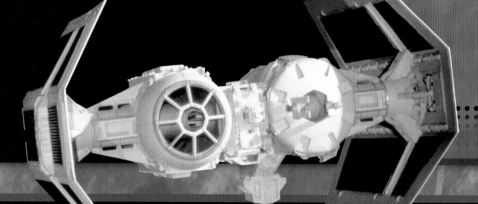

C-3PO
QUIZ

QUESTION 61

What was IG-88's profession?

A	A PROTOCOL DROID	☐
B	A BOUNTY HUNTER	☐
C	A MEDICAL DROID	☐

QUESTION 62

What colour was Obi-Wan Kenobi's lightsaber?

A	RED	☐
B	GREEN	☐
C	BLUE	☐

QUESTION 63

Who was married to Shmi Skywalker?

A	CLIEGG LARS	☐
B	OWEN LARS	☐
C	OBI -WAN KENOBI	☐

QUESTION 64

What is this alien species called?

A	TUSKEN RAIDERS	☐
B	GEONOSIANS	☐
C	JAWAS	☐

COUNT DOOKU

Homeworld: Serenno

Species: Human

Gender: Male

Height: 1.93 meters

Weapon: Lightsaber

Vehicle: Geonosian speeder, Geonosian solar sailer

Affiliation: Sith, Confederacy of Independent Systems, Jedi Order

Count Dooku was a powerful leader and a master swordsman. His prowess with a lightsaber was unparalleled and rather unusual as he used a fencing style unlike the rest of his former Jedi allies. At just thirteen years old he was chosen to be the Padawan of Thame Cerulian and began his training at the Jedi Temple. Dooku never fully gave his allegiance to the Jedi and always remained rather independent, something he shared with a lot of his pupils later in his life, most notably, Qui-Gon Jinn. A strong-minded man, Dooku's ideas were often out of step with those of the Jedi Council, despite the fact that his former mentor, Yoda, held a lofty position in that governing body, and it was a great blow to the Jedi Order when Count Dooku voluntarily renounced his commission.

Dooku was a political idealist. He felt that the Jedi weakened themselves by serving an institution as corrupt as the Republic. After his departure he disappeared for years, re-emerging as a political firebrand fanning the flames of rebellion in the galaxy. In an alarmingly short time, Dooku rallied thousands of systems to his cause, building a growing Separatist movement that threatened to split the Republic. At the end of the Clone Wars, the Separatists staged a daring strike against the Republic. The Confederacy had penetrated Coruscant's defences and absconded away with the kidnapped Chancellor Palpatine.

Obi-Wan Kenobi and Anakin Skywalker were sent to rescue Palpatine but it was all a setup. Dooku incapacitated Obi-Wan leaving Anakin to battle him alone. Anakin gained the advantage on his foe by severing both Dooku's hands. Palpatine then ordered Anakin to execute Dooku. Dooku realized he was expendable. Skywalker was the true prize, the gifted apprentice, the new Sith.

STAR
WARS

ALIEN RACES
QUIZ

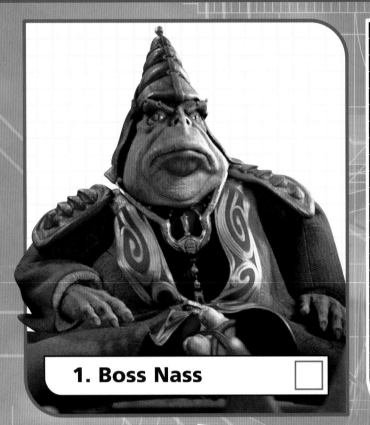

1. Boss Nass ☐

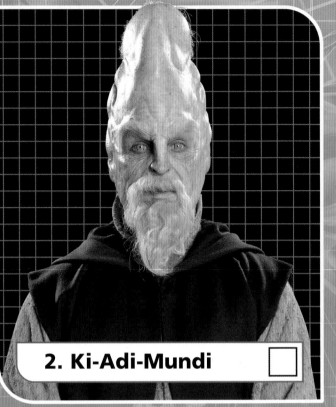

2. Ki-Adi-Mundi ☐

A. Cerean   **B. Gungan**   **C. Toydarian**   **D. Dug**

3. Sebulba ☐

4. Chewbacca ☐

CAN YOU MATCH EACH PICTURE OF THESE ALIENS TO THEIR SPECIES NAME?

5. Watto ☐

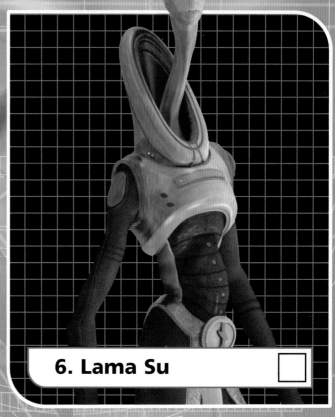

6. Lama Su ☐

E. Geonosian   F Trandoshan   G Kaminoan   H Wookiee

7. Bossk ☐

8. Poggle The Lesser ☐

ANSWERS

PAGES 8 & 9 C-3P0 QUIZ

1.C, 2.C, 3.B, 4.A, 5.B, 6.A, 7.B, 8. Darth Maul = C, Count Dooku = A, Mace Windu = B

PAGES 10 & 11 C-3P0 QUIZ

9.C, 10.B, 11.A, 12.A, 13.A, 14.C, 15.B, 16.C

PAGE 16 WORD SEARCH

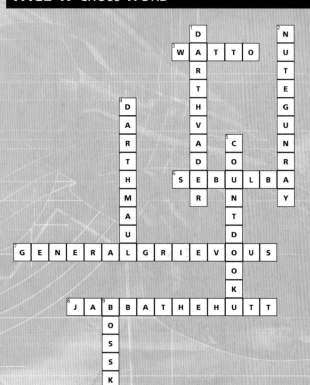

PAGE 17 CROSS WORD

PAGES 22 & 23 C-3P0 QUIZ

17.A, 18.B, 19.A, 20.A, 21.A, 22.B, 23.C, 24.A

PAGES 24 & 25 C-3P0 QUIZ

25.B, 26.C, 27.B, 28.B, 29.B, 30.A, 31. Darth Vader = C, Obi-Wan Kenobi = A, Yoda = B, 32.B

PAGES 38 & 39 *STAR WARS* ANAGRAMS

1. Mace Windu
2. Darth Vader
3. Luke Skywalker
4. Padmé Amidala
5. Anakin Skywalker
6. Obi-Wan Kenobi
7. Darth Maul
8. Count Dooku
9. Jar Jar Binks
10. Han Solo

PAGES 42 & 43 STARSHIP EXAM

1. X-wing starfighter
2. *Millennium Falcon*
3. TIE fighter
4. Super Star Destroyer
5. Jedi starfighter
6. *Slave I*

PAGES 46 & 47 C-3P0 QUIZ

33.B, 34.A, 35.A, 36.B, 37.A, 38.A, 39.A, 40.B

PAGES 48 & 49 C-3P0 QUIZ

41.B, 42.A, 43.B, 44.C, 45.A, 46.C, 47.A, 48.C

PAGES 58 & 59 C-3P0 QUIZ

49.C, 50.B, 51.B, 52.A, 53.C, 54.A, 55.C, 56.A

PAGES 60 & 61 C-3P0 QUIZ

57.A, 58.B, 59.A, 60.A, 61.B, 62.C, 63.A, 64.A

PAGES 66 & 67 ALIEN RACES QUIZ

1.B, 2.A, 3.D, 4.H, 5.C, 6.G, 7.F, 8.E